The Wise Bear Stories
Helping you through life's journey

Fair Exchange:
everyone wins

Scott Cranfield

Illustration Raphilena Bonito

The Wise Bear Stories
Fair Exchange: everyone wins
Scott Cranfield

ISBN 9781912821051

A CIP catalogue record for this book
is available from the British Library.

Published 2019
Tricorn Books
Aspex Gallery, 42 The Vulcan Building
Gunwharf Quays
Portsmouth PO1 3BF

Printed & bound in the UK

The Wise Bear Stories

Fair Exchange: everyone wins

How it Started:

Scott Cranfield the Author of Wise Bear has coached at the highest level for over 30 years, appearing on TV, radio, magazines, as well as hosting multiple seminars and being a key note speaker. His coaching covers subjects from life coaching and family relationships, to sport and business.

Since a young age I have been fascinated with and studied ways to help myself and others live the most inspired and fulfilled life possible. My journey has involved travelling the World attending countless programs and courses covering just about every area of life with the World's leading teachers.

As a father I wanted to share the best of what I had learnt with my children. I found a very effective way of doing this was through bedtime stories. I would create stories involving the challenges and anxieties my children had experienced that day and at the centre of each story is a character called Wise Bear. During the story the children would share with Wise Bear what was upsetting them or causing them to feel anxious. Wise Bear would use his vast experience and wisdom and share a whole new way of looking at these concerns to bring a calming balance to the children's mind, a balance they couldn't find on their own.

In each story the children learn useful tools and actions they can then apply for the rest of their lives.

My whole family are involved in bringing these stories to life, and it is our wish that these stories now help many other children and families, in the way they have helped ours.

Who is Wise Bear:

Wise Bear has been in the same family for generations. He has developed a unique wisdom that allows him to guide children, helping them dissolve their anxieties, as well as helping them make sense of the different challenges and events they experience in their lives. Every story covers a different subject, but within each story Wise Bear offers timeless lessons and vital life skills to help children navigate the journey of their life.

The lessons from Wise Bear will bring a calming balance to your children's mind, and give them a new and empowering perspective on any anxieties or challenges they face.

Even at 100 years old Wise Bear is still fascinated to learn and develop himself. He has had many brilliant teachers along the way, one special one he affectionately refers to as Dr D.

Wise Bear loves to read, exercise, make healthy smoothies and meditate. The only thing that gives away his age are some of his quirky sayings!

More than a story:
Each story ends with an affirmation and a short exercise to reinforce the lesson you have been reading about. This is a great opportunity to work with your children and help them apply the lessons directly to their own life.

Affirmations are a powerful way to develop strong and empowering beliefs for children, and the exercises give the children the opportunity to work through some of the challenges they face, so they can dissolve the anxieties and negative effects they hold in their mind.

Fair exchange

It was Friday afternoon and school had just finished. Toby and Alex were waiting outside for Mum. They spotted her walking into the playground and ran up to her.

Alex gave Mum a big hug. It was the weekend!

Toby didn't look so pleased.

Tugging at her sleeve urgently, he said, "Jake's mum just gave him some pocket money!"

"That's nice, dear," Mum replied, her mind elsewhere.

Toby looked unhappy and disgruntled.

"Mum, why don't I get pocket money?" he demanded, a little louder than before.

Mum turned to Toby, surprised.

"You do get pocket money, Toby. Each week you do your chores around the house and then I give you some money," replied Mum, calmly.

"Yes, I know that," he said impatiently. "But Jake didn't have to do anything to get his money! Not even put away his clothes!"

Mum took a deep breath and walked the children to the car.

On the journey home the conversation continued, Toby still thinking it was hugely unfair that he had to do jobs for his pocket money. Why couldn't he just be given money like Jake? He had been trying to save up to buy a skateboard, but it was taking so long.

Alex kept out of it. She could tell that Mum wasn't going to give in.

Toby had been silently brooding for the rest of the

afternoon and throughout dinner time. At bedtime, he thought he'd try his luck again and asked if he could get some money without doing any jobs.

"Toby, you really should be getting to sleep, but before you do, I think you should go and ask Wise Bear if he thinks it's fair to get pocket money without doing chores," said Mum, starting to lose patience. "And be quick!"

"OK. I'll talk to Wise Bear. I bet he'll understand," Toby replied, confident that he would see the injustice.

Toby got out of bed and went to Wise Bear's room. A light shone from the room, so he knew Wise Bear was still awake.

Toby knocked on the door.

He heard some rustling from inside.

"Sounds like Wise Bear is busy with something," Toby muttered under his breath.

"Wise Bear, can I ask you something?" he asked, pushing the door open a little. He could see Wise Bear through the crack, getting up from his chair.

"Yes, that's OK Toby, I was just watching a cookery programme on TV. It's all about making healthy meals.

I think I'm going to try one tomorrow – brown rice, kale and broccoli. I think it will be lovely with salmon," said Wise Bear, walking towards the door. Toby could hear him licking his lips.

The door opened fully and there stood Wise Bear, his chestnut fur slightly ruffled.

"What's on your mind?" asked Wise Bear, gesturing Toby to come inside.

"I don't think it's fair that I have to do chores to earn pocket money. I'm only 10. I should get it for nothing. My friends do," said Toby indignantly.

"Crikey! Well, Toby, I know you are only 10 years old, but some of the things you learn as a young lad can make a big difference in your life as you grow up, so let's discuss this some more.

"Let's start by looking at this completely differently. What would you like to do when you grow up?" Wise Bear said slowly.

"Hmmm, I don't really know," said Toby, curious as to where this was going to lead.

"Well, whatever it is, would you like to be successful?" replied Wise Bear.

"Yes of course! Who wouldn't want to be successful?" said Toby.

"Then there are certain principles you need to understand, and when you do your chances of being successful are far greater. Let me explain them to you." Wise Bear settled down into his seat and Toby sat next to him.

"I would like to tell you about the lesson of 'fair exchange'," began Wise Bear.

"What's fair exchange?" asked Toby, befuddled by the idea.

"Fair exchange is when the rewards you receive match the value you offer."

"I don't understand," replied Toby.

"Well, the reward you want is pocket money," said Wise Bear. "And the value your Mum wants in return is some jobs completed around the house.

"If you do the jobs properly, your Mum will be happy and she will reward you with pocket money. That's fair exchange."

Wise Bear relaxed back into his seat, his arms crossed.

"Does that make sense?" he asked.

"Yes it does," said Toby. "But I still don't think I should have to do the chores to get pocket money. I am only 10 after all and there is plenty of time for this fair exchange thingy as I get older."

Wise Bear laughed and then leant forward, his nose close to Toby's face.

"Toby, some principles are best learnt early in life because they will then become second nature to you, giving you lots of benefits. Let's look at this some more.

"Can you think of an example where someone has created lots of value for others and in return they have received big rewards? It could be anything, from a local shop or something you have seen on TV."

Toby thought for a moment.

"I see lots of people using the same smart phone that Mum has and I know she uses her phone a lot so others must as well. So that company has created lots of value and in return they sell lots of phones."

Wise Bear was impressed.

"Splendid! That's a good example, Toby. I will give you a more local example," he said.

"The butchers you take me to offer very good quality food with a very good service and they are also successful."

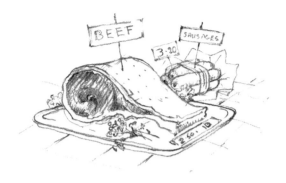

"Yes, they always seem busy," said Toby.

Wise Bear continued.

"If you want to be successful, it will help you to remember this golden rule of fair exchange.

"If you want something from somebody, make sure you do something in return that is valuable to them. This way both people get what they want."

Toby was listening carefully.

"It is the same if you want to sell something. You must make sure that what you are selling offers fair value for the price you are asking.

"Are you following this lesson, Toby?"

Toby sat up straight, his brow furrowed with concentration.

"Yes, it's beginning to help and make sense," he replied, thinking carefully.

But then Toby abruptly sat up and stuck out his lower lip.

"Hang on, though. Jake gets pocket money and he doesn't do anything for it. That's not fair exchange."

"Yes that's right, Toby. But when things are out of fair exchange they won't last because someone will eventually be unhappy and become annoyed.

"You might find Jake's mum will get really cross with Jake for never helping out around the house."

Toby quickly jumped in.

"Well, yes, she does. Jake told me that she got really cross with him the other day for not tidying his room."

"I'm not surprised," said Wise Bear smiling gently.

"Toby, you might think Mum is being tough on you,

but she is actually helping you learn a very important principle that will serve you for the rest of your life."

Wise Bear could see Toby was thinking, so he stopped to let the lesson sink in.

After a brief pause, he turned to Toby.

"Everything alright?"

Toby furrowed his brow again. He had a question.

"Does that mean when Mum and Dad ask me to do chores in exchange for pocket money, that they are teaching me the principle of fair exchange?"

"That's exactly right, Toby," said Wise Bear.

Toby nodded to himself.

"Now to really help you understand this, let's look at it in a different way.

"Imagine you did get pocket money for nothing. What would be the drawbacks of that?" asked Wise Bear.

Toby was tempted to be cheeky and say he couldn't see any drawbacks! But his mind was quick to see them and so he was very honest with his reply.

"I think it would make me lazy and I would probably waste the money instead of saving some of it."

He took a deep breath and continued.

"I might also expect others to do everything for me, which means I won't learn to look after myself properly. Maybe I wouldn't work as hard to achieve the things I would love to achieve.

"Oh, Wise Bear it does annoy me sometimes when you share a different way of looking at things, because I really have to think hard and change the way I see things!"

Wise Bear had a little chuckle to himself. He knew Toby wasn't really annoyed, it was just a figure of speech, and he was actually really pleased with Toby's answers.

"But I know you're right," continued Toby. "Although getting something for nothing might be nice at the time I can see it can cause more problems in the long run. So, thank you... I think!" said Toby with a wry smile.

"Toby, these are very good points," said Wise Bear, grinning. "If you did get money for nothing I think you would be in for a big shock when you get older and want to be successful."

"Yes, I can now see that there are lots of problems when getting something for nothing," Toby added.

"Toby, I think you have learnt the principle of fair exchange. How do you now feel about Mum asking you to do chores?"

"I must admit at first I was very annoyed at her, but now I understand, and I am grateful to her for teaching me this great principle!"

With that, Toby gave a big yawn.

"Looks like someone is relaxed and ready for sleep!" said Wise Bear, stifling a yawn himself.

"Yes, thank you Wise Bear," said Toby. "Goodnight."

"Goodnight, Toby."

About three weeks later Toby had seen the exact skateboard he wanted to buy – it was more expensive than he thought. He was just about to ask Mum if she would give him some money for it when he remembered the lesson of fair exchange.

He ran off to his room and wrote down all the extra chores he could do around the house that would really help Mum. With his list in his hand, he found Mum.

"Mum! I've seen this new skateboard that I REALLY want to save up for. If I do the chores on this list, will you give me extra pocket money?" Toby asked eagerly.

Mum looked at the list and with just a few changes agreed that if Toby did these jobs to a good standard it would be a big help to her and she would be happy to give Toby extra pocket money towards the skateboard.

Now Toby couldn't wait to get on with the chores!

Wise Bear Affirmation: What you say to yourself can make a big difference to how you think.
That's why Wise Bear always recommends an affirmation to help you remember his stories.
Here is today's one...

"*with fair exchange everyone wins*"

Wise Bear recommends repeating these affirmations regularly. You can say them either out loud or inside your head.

Use the questions below to discuss with your children and family how Wise Bear thinking can help you.

This exercise is designed to help your children 'think big' and to see what is possible with fair exchange.

Write below 10 examples of individuals or companies who have created significant value for others through their products or services and in return have received big rewards. This could be anything from global companies to local ones.

Here are two examples to start you off:

Individuals or companies that offer fair exchange.	What is it they do that offers great value?	How do they get rewarded?.
Local drama club	teachers work really hard to help the kids learn and have fun	Their classes are full up and they have a waiting list

Individuals or companies that offer fair exchange.	What is it they do that offers great value?	How do they get rewarded?.

Individuals or companies that offer fair exchange.	What is it they do that offers great value?	How do they get rewarded?